PATCHOGUE-MEDFORD LIBRARY

D1247058

PATCHOGUE-MEDFORD LIBRARY

PATCHOGUE-MEDFORD LIBRARY

THEATRE ROYAL—DRURY LANE

The Theatre Royal Drury Lane Production of

SHOW BOAT

[vocal score]

A MUSICAL PLAY

Adapted from Edna Ferber's novel of the same name

MUSIC BY

JEROME KERN

1885-1945

BOOK AND LYRICS BY

OSCAR HAMMERSTEIN 2nd

All rights reserved. This publication may not be resold, or let on hire, and no part of it may be reproduced or transmitted by any means (including photocopying) without the written permission of the copyright holder.

CHAPPELL & CO. LTD.	T. B. HARMS COMPANY
50, NEW BOND STREET, LONDON, W.1 and SYDNEY	62-64, WEST 45TH STREET NEW YORK

COPYRIGHT MCMXXVIII BY T. B. HARMS COMPANY

ALL RIGHTS RESERVED

PRINTED IN ENGLAND.

Q
782.8154
KER

c.1

SHOW BOAT

CAST OF CHARACTERS

(In the order of their appearance)

WINDY	JACK MARTIN
STEVE	COLIN CLIVE
PETE	FRED HEARNE
QUEENIE	ALBERTA HUNTER
PARTHY ANN HAWKS	VIOLA COMPTON
CAPTAIN ANDY	CEDRIC HARDWICKE
ELLIE	DOROTHY LENA
FRANK	LESLIE SARONY
RUBBER FACE	HENRY THOMAS
JULIE	MARIE BURKE
GAYLORD RAVENAL	HOWETT WORSTER
VALLON	PERCY PARSONS
MAGNOLIA	EDITH DAY
JOE	PAUL ROBESON
FARO DEALER	WILLIAM WALLACE
GAMBLER	ALEC J. WILLARD
LOUNGER	FELIX HILL
BACKWOODSMAN	ROY EMERTON
JEB	GORDON CROCKER
LA BELLE FATIMA	LENORE GADSDEN
OLD SPORT	CECIL DEREHAM
LANDLADY	MARGARET YARDE
ETHEL	KATHLEEN THOMAS
KIM (as Young Woman)	EDITH DAY
JAKE (Piano Player)	MICHAEL COLE
MAX	WILL STUART
MAN (with Guitar)	WALTER WEBSTER
CHARLIE (Doorman at Trocadero)	NORRIS SMITH
LOTTIE	NANCY BROWN
DOLLY	PEGGY LOVAT
HAZEL	ANN BARBOUR

Mississippi Chorus led and directed by John Payne

PML

SYNOPSIS OF SCENES

ACT I

SCENE 1. The Levee at Natchez on the Mississippi—*in the late Eighteen-eighties.*

SCENE 2. Kitchen Pantry of the " Cotton Blossom "—*a Half Hour Later.*

SCENE 3. Outside a Waterfront Gambling Saloon—*Simultaneous with Scene* 2.

SCENE 4. Auditorium and Stage of the " Cotton Blossom "—*One Hour Later.*

SCENE 5. Box-office, on Foredeck of the " Cotton Blossom "—*Three Weeks Later.*

SCENE 6. Auditorium and Stage of the " Cotton Blossom "—During the Third Act of " The Parson's Bride "—*That Evening.*

SCENE 7. The Top Deck of the " Cotton Blossom " —*Later that Night.*

SCENE 8. The Levee—*Next Morning.*

ACT II

SCENE 1. A Midway Plaisance, Chicago World's Fair, 1893.

SCENE 2. A Room on Ontario Street, 1904.

SCENE 3. Rehearsal Room of the Trocadero Music Hall—*About* 5 *p.m.*

SCENE 4. Trocadero Music Hall—*New Year's Eve,* 11.30, 1904.

SCENE 5. In front of the Office of " The Natchez Evening Democrat," 1927.

SCENE 6. Top Deck of the new " Cotton Blossom," 1927.

SCENE 7. Levee at Natchez—*the Next Night.*

Scenery Designed and Painted by JOSEPH AND PHIL HARKER.

Dances and Ensembles by MAX SCHECK.

Orchestra under the Direction of HERMAN FINCK.

The Play Produced by FELIX EDWARDES

SHOW BOAT

Pencil annotations indicate sequence & cuts on recording:
EMI CDC 7 49847 2

OVERTURE

Lyrics by
OSCAR HAMMERSTEIN IInd

Music by
JEROME KERN

ALL RIGHTS RESERVED.
Copyright, MCMXXVIII, by T. B. HARMS Co
Chappell & Co., Ltd., 50, New Bond Street, London, W.1 & Sydney.

29678

② Ben sostenuto

③

Chappell

Chappell

9

9678

Chappell

Chappell

No. 1

Opening Act I
The Levee At Natchez On The Mississippi

Lyrics by
OSCAR HAMMERSTEIN IInd

Music by
JEROME KERN

Coloured folks work on de Mis-si-sip-pi, Coloured folks work while de

Chappell

Chappell

14

29678

Chappell

16

Chappell

Moderato

Queenie waddles on from market with basket of provisions on her head.

Trumpet

Oboe

Strings

Fl.

(commodo)
As Queenie moves toward boat, Pete sees brooch on her collar and questions its source.

Cello

(Exit Queenie, chuckling)

cresc.

rall.

Trpts.

Chappell

29678

Chappell

Capriccioso
Enter a group of mincing misses.

Fl. *p*

Violin

(Cross over)

B'ss'n

stacc.

Chappell

Chappell

Chappell

Chappell

24

Chappell

Lo stesso tempo

Girls & Boys:
Cap - tain An - dy has gath - ered a troupe in the

Coloured Chorus:
Ho!

Ho!

rall. poco a poco

Girls & Boys:
great - est of dram-mers and jol - ly co-me-dies, Ste-phen Ba - ker, the

Coloured Chorus:
Ho!

Chappell

26

Chappell

Chappell

28

29678

Chappell

Parthy Ann appears. "Andy Hawks! Drat that man, He's never around!"

Adagio pesante (falteringly)

Piano off stage

(Dialogue)

The band appears, led by Captain Andy with a couple of town girls on each arm.

(Orchestra)

Chappell

Allegretto

GIRLS
Cap-tain An-dy, Cap-tain An-dy, here's your le-mon cake and home made can-dy.

Quince pre-serve and ap-ple brand-y; Ma-ma sends her best re-gards to you.

GIRLS & BOYS
Cap-tain An-dy, Cap-tain An-dy, we've been hear-ing all a-bout your dan-dy

show. Is this year's good as last year? Won't you tell us what is new?

Chappell

Captain Andy's Bally-Hoo

Chappell

32

29678   Chappell

show sound dan - dy. Frank and El - lie, c'mon let's show them

just a sam - ple of your soft shoe dance! Cap - tain An - dy,

Cap - tain An - dy, Just a sam - ple. What a man! My land, he

gives a - way his show for noth - ing! Just a sam - ple of the dance.

Chappell

Dancette.. ELLIE & FRANK.

STEVE: "I reckon, I won't do any more talkin' about it."

Chappell

Chappell

36

29678   Chappell

38

(Exit Vallon)

C Andante moderato

mp RAVENAL

Who cares if my boat goes up stream,— or if the

gale bids me go with the riv-er's flow?——

Chappell

Piano off stage. Ravenal listens, amused at the poor rendition.

Chappell

The drift wood float-ing o-ver the sea Some day finds a shel-ter-ing lee,

So some-where there sure-ly must be A har-bour meant for me.

RAVENAL

(Orch.)

Chappell

Chappell

Moderato *molto espressivo through dialogue.*

Chappell

Chappell

Make-Believe
(Ravenal and Magnolia)

RAVENAL

On - ly

make be - lieve — I love you, — On - ly

make be - lieve — that you love me. — Oth - ers

find peace of mind in pre - tend - ing; — Could - n't

Chappell

you? could-n't I? could-n't we? _____ Make be-

lieve our lips _____ are blend-ing _____ In a

phan-tom kiss, _____ or two, or three. _____ Might as

well make be-lieve I love you, _____ For, to

Chappell

(Magnolia draws back)

tell the truth,—— I do.—— Your par-don I

pray,—— 'Twas too much to say —— the words that be-

MAGNOLIA

tray my heart.—— We on-ly pre-

tend,—— You do not of-fend —— In play-ing a

Chappell

Allegretto

MAGNOLIA
The game of just sup-pos-ing is the sweet-est game I know;—

Our dreams are more ro-man-tic than the world we see.

RAVENAL
And if the things we dream a-bout don't hap-pen to be so,—

48

That's just an un-im-port-ant tech-ni-cal-i-ty.

Poco animato

MAGNOLIA

Tho' the cold and brut-al fact is You and I have nev-er

met. We need not mind con-ven-tion's

P's and Q's,——— If we put our thoughts in

Ob.

(con Ped.)

29678

Chappell

prac - tice, We can ban-ish all re - gret Im-ag-in-ing 'most an-y - thing we choose.

dolce
We could make be-lieve I love you, We could make be-lieve That you love me. Oth - ers find peace of

Chappell

Chappell

Molto lento

pp
lunga

con Ped.

(Ravenal and Vallon exit)

L.H.

♩ = 80 *Dialogue between Magnolia and Joe*

pp

Exit Magnolia

L.H.

rall.

attacca

Chappell

Ol' Man River

(Joe and Male Chorus)

Chappell

54

29678

Chappell

You an' me we sweat an' strain,
Bod-y all ach-in' an' racked wid pain. "Tote dat barge!"
"Lift dat bale!" Git a lit-tle drunk an' you'll
land in jail. Ah gits wear-y an' sick of try-in', Ah'm

Chappell

tired of liv-in' an' scared of dy-in', But ol' man Riv-er, He

f cresc.

jes' keeps rol-lin' a - lon!

allarg. *ffz* *fp* Horns

Moderato
pp

Col - oured folks work on de Mis - sis - sip - pi,

(Stevedores appear carrying various loads and group around Joe)

pp

(Curtains close in on group)

Col-oured folks work while de white folks play Pul-lin' dose boats, from de

Chappell

Chappell

58

29678

Chappell

Chappell

Chappell

Chappell

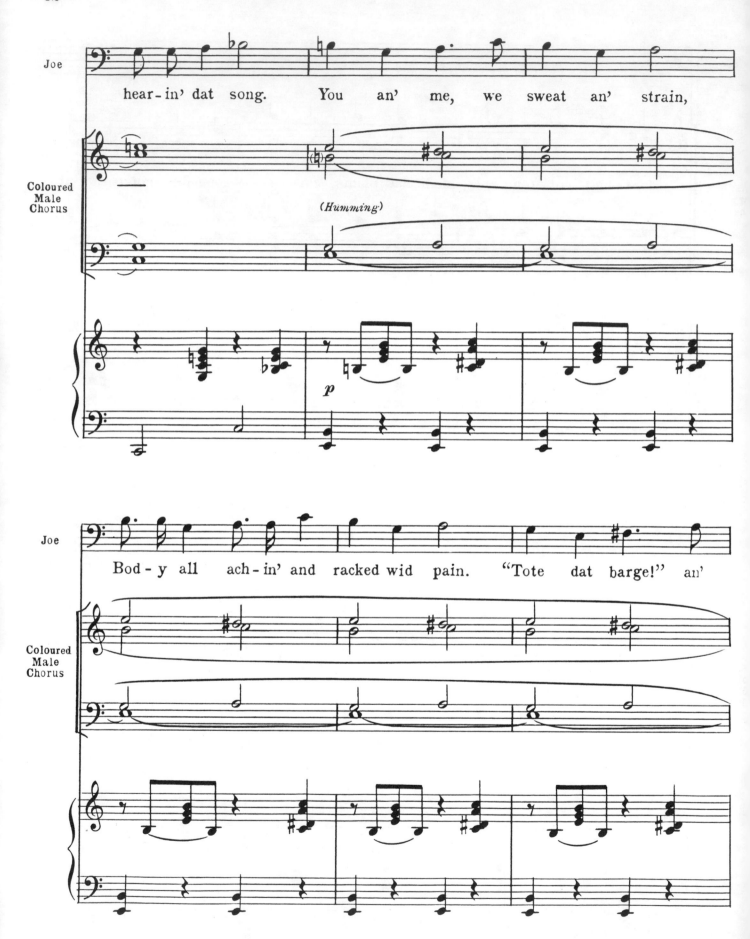

Chappell

Joe: Lift dat bale!" We gits a lit-tle drunk an' we

Joe / Coloured Male Chorus: lands in jail. Ah gits wear-y an' sick of try-in', Ah'm

Coloured Male Chorus: Ah gits wear-y an' sick of try-in', Ah'm

29678

Chappell

63

Chappell

Scene II

Kitchen Pantry of the "Cotton Blossom"

Allegro con brio

Piano

Curtain
Moderato   *Magnolia is discovered seated at the table.*

Horn

Cl.

Chappell

66

Chappel

Can't Help Lovin' Dat Man

(Julie, Queenie, Magnolia, Joe and Mixed Quartet)

Fish got to swim—and birds got to fly,— I got to love—one man till I die,— Can't help lov-in' dat man— of mine. Tell me he's la - zy, Tell me he's slow,— Tell me I'm cra - zy, may-be, I know.—

Chappell

can't help lov-in' dat man— of mine. *(Through dialogue)*

Solo Violin

pp

p JULIE

Oh, lis-ten, sis-ter, I love my Mis-ter man —— and I can't-

p

Chappe

Chappell

man till I die,— Can't help lov-in' dat man— of

mine.————————— Tell me he's la - zy,

tell me he's slow,— Tell me I'm cra - zy, may-be I know,—

Can't help lov-in' dat man — of mine. ————————

Chappell

Chappell

Chappell

Chappell

senza voce 2nda volta

Chappell

Chappell

Chappell

Chappell

Chappell

Chappell

Chappell

(For encore see top of page 75.)

Chappell

Scene III
Outside A Waterfront Saloon

Chappell

Ellie reappears. *She passes by* *Ravenal and drops her handkerchief; Ravenal restores it politely to her hand.*

Dialogue ELLIE and RAVENAL

A la valse

Exit Ravenal

lunga pausa

Chappell

No. 7 6

Life On The Wicked Stage

(Ellie and Girls)

18 ms. cut

hold your hand, (which means an ex - tra beer or sand - wich)

Ev - 'ry - bod - y whis - pers: "Ain't her life a whirl?"____

Though you're warned a - gainst a rou - é ru - in - ing your re - pu -

- ta - tion, When you've played a - round the one night trade A - round a

Chappell

88

great big na - tion, Wild old men who give you

jewels and sab - les On - ly live in Ae - sop's Fa - bles.

Girls

Though we've lis-ten'd to you

Ellie

Life up-on the wick-ed stage is no-thing for a girl! ——

Chappell

GIRLS
moan and grieve, You must par-don us if we do not be-lieve you,

There is no doubt you're cra-zy a -bout your aw - ful stage.

ELLIE
I ad-mit it's fun to smear my face with paint Caus - ing ev - 'ry one to

think I'm what I ain't, And I like to play a de - mi mond - y

Chappell

role with soul! Ask the he-ro does he like the way I lure

When I play a hus-sy or a par-a-mour, Yet when once the cur-tain's

poco rit

down my life is pure And how I dread it!

colla voce

a tempo. *mf* GIRLS

Life up-on the wick-ed stage ain't ev-er what a girl sup-

mf a tempo.

Chappell

Chappell

Chappell

Chappell

Till Good Luck Comes My Way

(Ravenal and Men)

lot — have their fate se-cure in a guard-ed spot of the world,

They're wel-come to their drab — ca - reer.

Poco meno

Men

It is all well e - nough to be grin-ning while your win-nings

It is ea - - sy to be grin-ning while your stack is

96

29678

Chappell

If I am los-ing to-day —— I will —— like you.

—— like you.

(RAVENAL) take my loss and I'll pay —— For I know ——

That in time my luck will

Chappell

98

29678   Chappell

Chappell

There may be sun-shine to - mor-row to fill the day. ——— While I've a heart and a brain And my eb - o - ny cane I can bor - row Un - til the day when good - luck comes my

Chappell

Chappell

102

29678

Chappell

Scene IV
Auditorium And Stage Of The "Cotton Blossom"

ANDY   *"Prompt her, Nola"*
MAGNOLIA *"Hamilton, my own!"* *"Papa! look at Julie!"*

Moderato misterioso
Melos
Misterioso
Viola Solo

Chappell

104

Chappell

Chappell

106

29678

Chappell

Andantino

Frank calls Ravenal in.   Joe is discovered in upper box of auditorium.

Chappell

Valse

Fl.

Solo Violin

pp

ten.

Violin

Chappell

Piu mosso
Enter Magnolia, followed by Julie

Lento assai

Dolce

Chappell

110

Tempo di Valse
Magnolia sees Ravenal

sempre pp

(pp)

L.H.

Moderato (enter Steve)

R.H.

pp

Chappell

Chappell

112

Lento

29678

Chappell

soon for-got-ten; But ol' man Riv-er he jes keeps roll-in' a-

lon?

espr.

Ravenal spoken: "I understand. Miss Lucy will you be mine?"

But

He kisses Magnolia.

poco a poco cresc.

ol' man Riv-er he just keeps roll-in' a-lon?

f cresc.

segue

Chappell

Scene V

In Front Of The Box-office, On Foredeck Of The "Cotton Blossom"

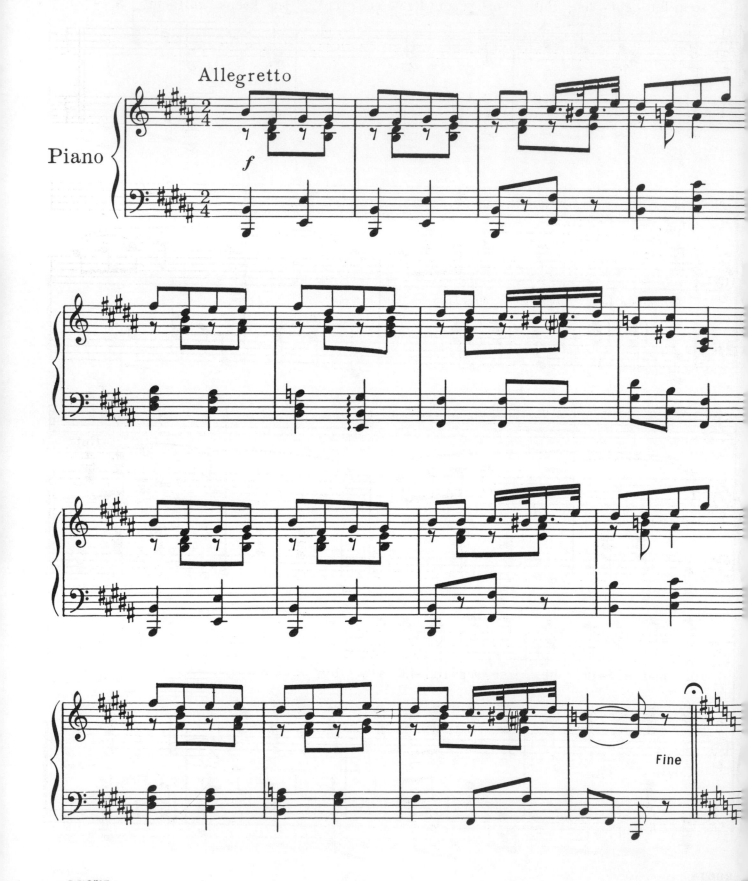

Allegretto

Piano

Fine

Chappell

I Might Fall Back On You

(Ellie and Frank)

Tempo di Polka

FRANK: Lit-tle girl you are safe with me: I can pro-tect what's mine; I am a sturd-y ma-ple tree and you're my cling-ing vine.

ELLIE: Woods are just full of ma-ple trees, Ce-dar and oak and pine; Let me look them o - ver, please, And

Chappe

then I'll let you know ————— If you have a show.

2nd volta FRANK & ELLIE (with added words)

Af-ter I have looked a-round the world for a mate—

Then, per-haps, I might fall back on you. ————

When I am con-vinced that there is no bet-ter fate—

Chappell

118

29678   Chappell

Chappell

When I am con-vinced that there is no bet-ter fate —

Then I might de-cide that you will do. —

Other group (to Ellie)

He is just an ave-rage lad, Though no gift to wo-man-hood,

Some girls say he's not so bad, Oth-ers say he's not so good!

Chappell

Chappell

122

29678

Chappell

Queenie's Bally - Hoo

(Queenie and Coloured Chorus)

What fo' you gals dress up dic - ty? Where's yo' all goin'?

Tell dose sting - y men of yours to step up here in

line.

Meno mosso

QUEENIE

C'mon, folks, we'se rar - in' to go, Is you or ain't you see-in' dis show?

Chappell

Chappell

QUEENIE

Two seats for twen-ty cents ain't so dear!

Dance. Vivo

mf

Chappell

Moderato *(Fox-trot tempo)*

Chappell

Chappell

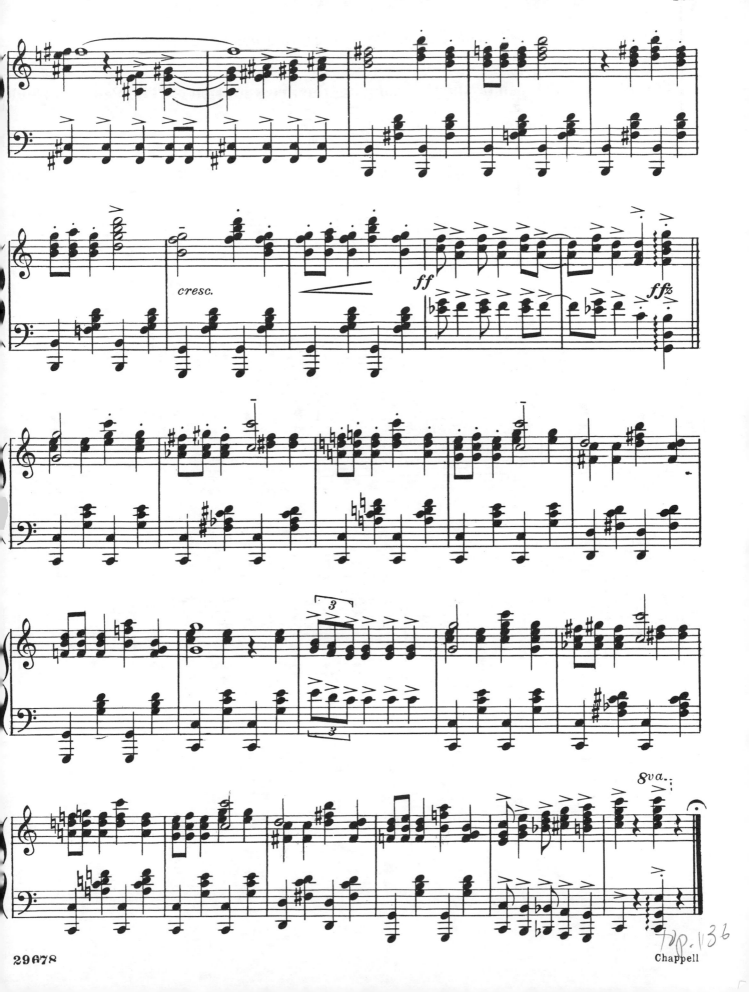

Chappell

Scene VI

Auditorium And Stage Of The"Cotton Blossom" During the Third Act of "The Parson's Brid

Incidental Music, played on the Stage during the presentation of "The Parson's Bride

VIOLIN

Small
Organ

Chappell

Andante

© *For Villain's Entrance*

Repeat ad lib.

Repeat from © ad lib.

Chappell

Villain's Dance
(Frank's specialty dance)

Chappell

Scene VII
The Upper Deck Of The "Cotton Blossom"

Introduction And Duet "You Are Love."

Chappell

Chappell

Chappell

You Are Love

Tempo di Valse   (Ravenal and Magnolia)

Once a wand-'ring ne'er-do - well,   Just a vag-rant rov-ing fel-low, I

went my way. ————— Life was just a joke to

tell   Like a lone-ly Punch-i - nel-lo My role was

gay. ———— But I knew the joke was aim - less, Time went on I

liked the game less, For you see, _____

Some-where lurked a spark di-vine, And I kept wond-'ring wheth-er mine Would

Poco agitato

come to me. _____ Then my

for-tune turned and I found you. Here _____ you

Chappell

are with my arms a - round you, You— will nev-er know what you've

meant— to me. MAGNOLIA You're— the prize that heav-en has sent— to

RAVENAL

me, Here's— a bright and beau-ti-ful world,— All

new wrapped up—— in you.——

Tempo di Valse

new wrapped up—— in you.——

Tempo di Valse

(rit)

p   *Cello*

Chappell

Chappell

142

29678

Chappell

appassionato
f TOGETHER

One truth for - ev - er true. You are

Love Won-der of all the world

Where you go with me Heav-en will al - ways

Where you go with me Heav-en will al - ways

Grandioso

Grandioso

Chappell

Scene VIII - Finale Act I

Levee Beside The "Cotton Blossom"

Chapp

Girls: -light-ed to be there when these u - nit-ed two are plight-ed to be one!

Boys: like theirs is not for ev-'ry - one!

Lo stesso tempo

Girls: Cap - tain An - dy! Cap - tain An - dy! My, but does-nt he look

Boys: Cap - tain An - dy! Cap - tain An - dy! My, but does-n't he look

Violins

Girls: fine and dan - dy! Now Mag - nol - ia's found her mate, You

Boys: fine and dan - dy! Now Mag - nol - ia's found her mate, You

Chappell

Chappell

Chappell

Chappell

We can hard-ly wait to see —— The fran-tic looks of the bride-groom and quakes of the bride whom he takes now or nev-er, and makes her for-ev-er the one and the on-ly one; Who will take care that his life's not a lone-ly one while she's the on-ly one.

cresc.

cresc.

molto marc.

ancora piu cresc.

Chappell

Enter Magnolia and Ravenal

Hap-py the bride ——— May the great-est of hap-pi-ness,

Hap-py the bride And may the great-est of hap-pi-ness,

health and wealth at - tend you, love-ly bride to be. There are

health and wealth at - tend you, love-ly bride to be. There are

few wed-ded to an-y-one charm-ing as you.

Pride to be

few wed-ded to an-y-one charm-ing as you.

Chappell

152

29678

Chappell

153

Moderato

you?

Fish got to swim— an birds got to fly,— I got to love— one
man till I die,— Can't help lov-in' dat man— of mine!
Tell me he's la - zy, tell me he's slow,— Tell me I'm cra - zy,

29678   Chappell

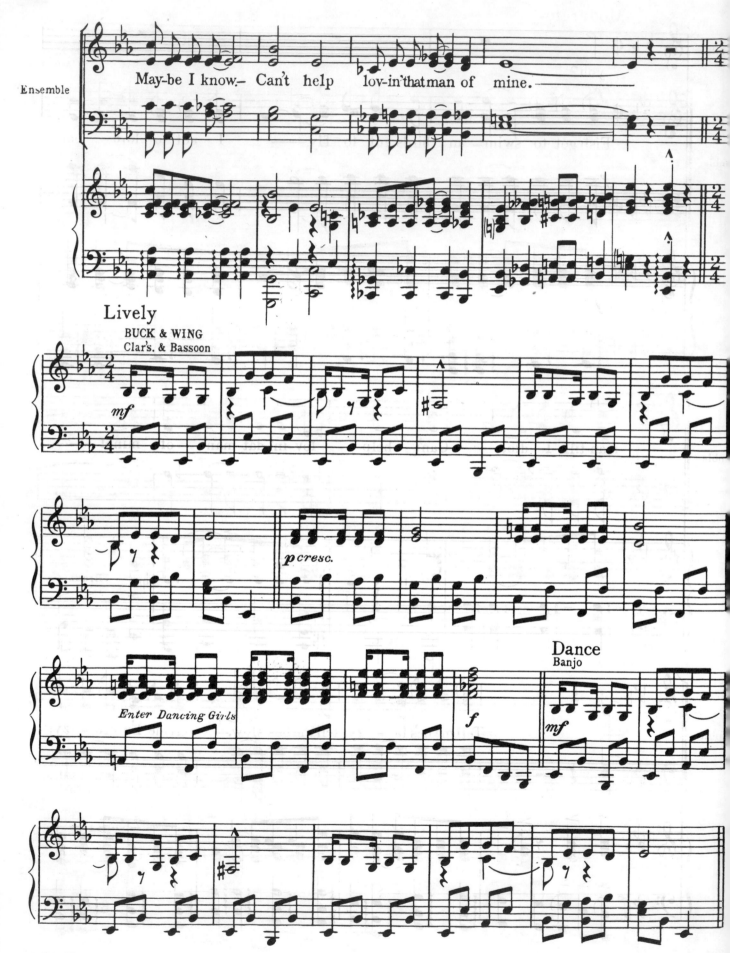

Ensemble

May-be I know.— Can't help lov-in' that man of mine.——

Lively

BUCK & WING
Clar's. & Bassoon

mf

p cresc.

Enter Dancing Girls

f

Dance
Banjo

mf

Chappell

Chappell

Tempo I

Ensemble

He can come home— as late as can be, Home with-out him— ain't

Ensemble

no home to me.— Can't help lov-in' dat man!—

Parthy "Stop them!"

Chappell

Chappell

Tempo I

Fish got to swim, and birds got to fly,— I got to love— one man till I die.—

allarg. **Grandioso**

Can't help lov-in' that man— of mine! ————

allargando *ff appassionato* **Grandioso**

Curtain

Chappell

Entr' Acte

No. 18

Chappell

Chappell

Prelude and Opening Act II
The Midway Plaisance At The Chicago World's Fair

No. 19

Chappell

164

Chapp

Chappell

Chapp

Chappell

168

29678

Chappell

Chappell

170

noth-ing wrong,— She's a prin-cess:———— From bet-ter folks than us I guess

Girls. You can stay, but I must run.

Boys All right! You al-ways spoil my fun.

sf

Vivace (♩ = ♪)

Chorus Belles and beaux, Dressed in the ve - - ry la - test

Chappell

Chappell

172

Chappell

Chappell

174

With their clothes all tai - lor made.

With their clothes the lat - est on the "Mid - way"

All their Coun-try Cou-sins gape and stare When they

see the dan-dies on Pa - rade.

sffz

D.S. for exit
(*senza voce*)

Chappel

Incidental
(Fatima's 2nd Dance)

D Tempo come prima

Why Do I Love You?

Magnolia, Ravenal, Cap. Andy, Parthy and Ensemble

No. 20

Moderato

MAGNOLIA

I'm walk - ing on the air, dear, —— For life is fair, dear, ——

Chappell

to lov - ers; I'm in ___ the sev-enth

heav - en ___ (There's more than sev - en, ___ my heart dis - cov -

RAVENAL

- ers,) In this sweet, im - pro-ba-ble and un - real

world, Find-ing you has giv-en me my i - deal world.

Chappell

MAGNOLIA

Why do I love you? Why do you love me?

TOGETHER

Why should there be two hap-py as we?——

RAVENAL

Can you see —— the why or where - fore

I should be —— the one you care for?

Chappell

MAGNOLIA

You're a luck-y boy, I am luck-y too,

TOGETHER

All our dreams of joy Seem to come true; ——

May-be that's —— be - cause you love me,

May - be that's why I love you! ——

Chappell

Chappell

Chappe

Chappell

Chappell

joy   seem to come true.—   May-be   that's —   be-cause you

love   me,   May-be that's why   I   love   you! —

Valse

Dance

mf dolce, con espressione

Chappell

A la Fox-Trot

CHORUS

You're a luck-y boy! I am luck-y too! All our dreams of

joy Seem to come true.—— May-be that's —— be-cause you

entrance Cap. Andy & Parthy

love me, May-be that's why I love you!

CAPTAIN ANDY

Why do I love you? Why do you love me? Why should there be

two hap-py as we? Can you see the why or

where - fore, I should be the one you care for?

Chappell

You're a luck-y boy, I am luck-y too, All our dreams of joy seem to come true.— May-be that's — be-cause you love me, May-be that's why I love you! ——

Dance (ANDY and PARTHY)

Chappell

You're a luck-y boy! I am luck-y too! All our dreams of joy Seem to come true. May-be that's be-cause I love you! May-be that's why I love you!

29678

Chappell

DAHOMEY
(Coloured Chorus)

Chappell

Chappell

Chappell

Chappell

COLOURED WOMEN only

White Chorus

Ah——— Ah   Ah——— Ah   Ah ah ah   ah ah ah

are   act – ing   vi –cious,   They might get ma – li –cious   And

are   act – ing   vi –cious,   They might get ma – li –cious   And

White Chorus

though I'm   not   fear – ful   I'll   not   be   a   spear – ful,   So

Chappe

Coloured Chorus

Ah — Ah Ah — Ah Ah ah ah ah ah ah

Ah — Ah Ah — Ah Ah ah ah ah ah ah

White Chorus

You'd bet-ter show me the way from Da-hom-ey!

Coloured Chorus

We're glad to see them go! ——

Chappell

194

Coloured Chorus

We're glad to see those white folks go!

Coloured Chorus

Dy-un-ga Doe! Dy-un-ga Doe!

Coloured Chorus

Dy-un-ga, Hun-gy ung gun-ga, Hun-gy ung gun-ga go!

29678

Chappe

Chappell

Chappell

Chappell

Chappell

Dance (Tempo I)

Chappell

Scene II
A Room On Ontario Street In Chicago

Moderato

Piano

pp

(This music is played while Ellie reads Ravenal's letter)

D.S.
for Curtain

Chappe

Scene III
Rehearsal Room Of The Trocadero Music Hall

BILL
(Julie)

No. 23

Words by
P. G. WODEHOUSE and
OSCAR HAMMERSTEIN IInd

Chappell

204

29678

Chappell

Chappell

[S] omitted

No. 24

Can't Help Lovin' Dat Man (Reprise)

(Magnolia)

Moderato

VOICE

Piano — p (Guitar)

Fish got to swim, and birds got to fly,—
I got to love one man till I die.— Can't help lov-in' dat man of mine!———
Tell me he's la-zy, tell me he's slow,—
Tell me I'm cra-zy, may-be, I know— Can't help lov-in' dat man of

Chappell

mine! ——— When he goes a - way That's a rain-y

day, And when he comes back that day is fine ——The sun will

cresc.

cresc.

shine. He can come home—as late as can be,— Home with-out him— ain't

p

p

no home to me,— Can't help lov-in' dat man of mine! ———

p lunga

Chappell

Allegro *Magnolia tries and fails to sing in this tempo.*

Chappell

Scene IV
Trocadero Music Hall

Captain Andy's Entrance

*) After The Ball
(Magnolia)

CHAS. K. HARRIS

Valse moderato

A lit-tle maid-en climbed an old man's knee, — Begged for a sto-ry, "Do, Un-cle,

Copyright MDCCCXCII by Chas. K. Harris
*) Rb-Copyright MCMXIX by Chas. K. Harris
Printed by permission of the publisher

please,———— Why are you sin - gle, why live a - lone?———— Have you no ba - bies? Have you no home?"———— "I had a sweet - heart years, years a - go;———— Where she is

now, pet, you will soon know. —— List' to the

sto - ry, I'll tell it all, —— I be-

-lieved her faith - less, af — ter the ball."

Moderato

Af-ter the ball is o - ver, Af-ter the break of morn, ——

Chappell

Af-ter the dan-cers leav - ing After the stars are gone; ——— Man-y a heart is ach - ing If you could read them all; ——— Man-y the hopes that have van - ished Af - ter the ball. ball.

Chimes (12 o'clock)

Scene V
In Front Of The Office Of "The Natchez Evening Democrat."

Ol' Man River (Reprise)
(Joe)

New things come 'n ole things go But all things look De same to Joe. Folks git mad An' starts a war, An' den git glad, Don't know what for. Ah keep laughin' In-stead of cry-in', Ah mus' keep liv-in' Un-til ah'm dy-in', But ol' man Riv-er, he jes' keeps roll-in' a - lon'!

Chappell

Scene VI
Top Deck Of The New "Cotton Blossom"

You Are Love (Reprise)
(Ravenal)

Chappell

Won - der of all the world, ———————— Where you go with me Heav - en will al - ways be. ———————

Chappell

Scene VII
Levee At Natchez

Piano

"Cot – ton Blos-som," "Cot – ton   Blos-som,"

Cap – tain An-dy's   float-ing   show,   Thrills and   laugh-ter,   Con - cert

af – ter,   Get your girl   and   go!   go!

Chappel

No. 28

Dance away the night
(Kim and Chorus)

Chappell

REFRAIN.

Dance ____ away the night ____ and we can all be hap-py till the morn - ing! Dance ____ away the night ____ and we can stick to - geth-er till the dawn! Blue ____ will turn to gray, ____ and when the moon steals off without a warn - ing,

non legato

mf-f

You_____ can turn and say_____ you're ve - ry glad you met us, And

then for-get us. But dance_____ away the night_____ and we can

all be hap-py till the morn - ing! Dance_____ away the

night_____ and we can stick to-geth-er till the dawn! dawn!_____

Chappell

PATTER
MEN.

If you want to dance ___ here's one who's clev - er;

Have a cav-a-lier ___ with style and tone. ___

If you're on your toes ___ and kind o' fol-low-where-he-goes ___ You'll find a

rhythm that you feel you could do with him for e - - ver.

Chappell

Get the band to break ___ in - to a fox - - trot

pp

Mean enough to make ___ the trees and rocks trot:

Then you won't stay still — you'll dance a - gainst your will, and

poco rall.

keep right on un - til the break of day! You pray to stay to

poco rall.

Chappell

REFRAIN.
OMNES

Dance _____ away the night _____ and we can all be hap-py till the

morn - ing! Dance _____ away the night _____ and we can

stick to - geth - er till the dawn! Blue _____ will turn to

GIRLS

gray, _____ and when the moon steals off without a warn - ing,

Chappell

You _____ can turn and say _____ you're ve - ry glad you met us, And

then for - get us. But dance _____ away the night _____ and we can

all be hap - py till the morn - ing! Dance _____ away the

night _____ and we can stick to - geth - er till the dawn! _____

Chappell

Finale

Chappell

Chappell

Chappell

Printed in Great Britain by Hobbs the Printers of Southampton 10/85

END OF OPERA